P9-DGE-802

Animals on the Farm

By JAN PFLOOG

A GOLDEN BOOK • NEW YORK

Western Publishing Company, Inc.
Racine, Wisconsin 53404

Copyright © 1968, 1963 by Western Publishing Company, Inc. All rights reserved. Printed in the U.S.A. No part of this book may be reproduced or copied in any form without written permission from the publisher. GOLDEN®, GOLDEN & DESIGN®, A LITTLE GOLDEN BOOK®, and A GOLDEN BOOK® are trademarks of Western Publishing Company, Inc. ISBN 0-307-02109-2

S T

Mother Duck and her ducklings
march through the farmyard.

Mother Cat watches over
her four fluffy kittens.

And Mother Collie Dog
tends to her playful pups.

Mother Turkey and her poults
are busy looking for food.

It's lunchtime for the piglets.

Mother Hen and her chicks
are eating, too.

Mother Goat and her frisky kids
play in the sun.

Mother Ewe and her little lamb
have soft, woolly coats.

Mother Goose and her goslings
are off to the pond.

Mother Cow gives her dusty calf a bath.

Mother Mare and her spindly-legged colt
graze in the pasture.

Mother Mouse and her baby mice
are feasting on an ear of corn.